The Music of
GEORGE GERSHWIN®
Plus One

20 Great Songs To Play With Orchestral Accompaniment CD

Arranged by Tony Esposito
Background instruments performed and arranged by Andy Selby

M378

1199

CONTENTS

BUT NOT FOR ME

Music and Lyrics by
GEORGE GERSHWIN and IRA GERSHWIN
Arranged by TONY ESPOSITO

IF9921CD

'S WONDERFUL

Music and Lyrics by
GEORGE GERSHWIN and IRA GERSHWIN
Arranged by TONY ESPOSITO

With a swing feel ♩ = 150 (♫ = ♪♪)

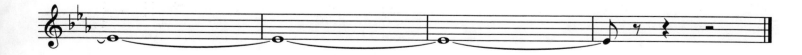

IF9921CD

EMBRACEABLE YOU

Music and Lyrics by
GEORGE GERSHWIN and IRA GERSHWIN
Arranged by TONY ESPOSITO

IF9921CD

FASCINATING RHYTHM

Music and Lyrics by
GEORGE GERSHWIN and **IRA GERSHWIN**
Arranged by TONY ESPOSITO

Moderately fast ♩ = 175

Swing

Tempo I

Swing

IF9921CD

I GOT PLENTY O' NUTTIN'

Music and Lyrics by
GEORGE GERSHWIN, DU BOSE
and DOROTHY HEYWARD and IRA GERSHWIN
Arranged by TONY ESPOSITO

IF9921CD

I GOT RHYTHM

Music and Lyrics by
GEORGE GERSHWIN and IRA GERSHWIN
Arranged by TONY ESPOSITO

LIZA

Lyrics by IRA GERSHWIN and GUS KAHN
Music by GEORGE GERSHWIN
Arranged by TONY ESPOSITO

THE LORELEI

Music and Lyrics by
GEORGE GERSHWIN and IRA GERSHWIN
Arranged by TONY ESPOSITO

THE MAN I LOVE

Music and Lyrics by
GEORGE GERSHWIN and IRA GERSHWIN
Arranged by TONY ESPOSITO

MINE

Music and Lyrics by
GEORGE GERSHWIN and IRA GERSHWIN
Arranged by TONY ESPOSITO

Moderate swing ♩ = 135

rit.

IF9921CD

NICE WORK IF YOU CAN GET IT

Music and Lyrics by
GEORGE GERSHWIN and **IRA GERSHWIN**
Arranged by TONY ESPOSITO

Fast swing, in 2 ♩ = 250

SLAP THAT BASS

Music and Lyrics by
GEORGE GERSHWIN and IRA GERSHWIN
Arranged by TONY ESPOSITO

OF THEE I SING
(Baby)

Music and Lyrics by
GEORGE GERSHWIN and IRA GERSHWIN
Arranged by TONY ESPOSITO

RIALTO RIPPLES

Music and Lyrics by
GEORGE GERSHWIN and IRA GERSHWIN
Arranged by TONY ESPOSITO

Moderate rag ♩ = 170

Rialto Ripples - 2 - 1
IF9921CD

OH, LADY BE GOOD!

Music and Lyrics by
GEORGE GERSHWIN and IRA GERSHWIN
Arranged by TONY ESPOSITO

SOMEONE TO WATCH OVER ME

Music and Lyrics by
GEORGE GERSHWIN and IRA GERSHWIN
Arranged by TONY ESPOSITO

IF9921CD

STRIKE UP THE BAND

Music and Lyrics by
GEORGE GERSHWIN and IRA GERSHWIN
Arranged by TONY ESPOSITO

Moderate march tempo ♩ = 180

SUMMERTIME

Music and Lyrics by
GEORGE GERSHWIN, DU BOSE
and DOROTHY HEYWARD and IRA GERSHWIN
Arranged by TONY ESPOSITO

IF9921CD

THEY ALL LAUGHED

Music and Lyrics by
GEORGE GERSHWIN and IRA GERSHWIN
Arranged by TONY ESPOSITO

THEY CAN'T TAKE THAT AWAY FROM ME

Music and Lyrics by
GEORGE GERSHWIN and IRA GERSHWIN
Arranged by TONY ESPOSITO

IF9921CD